Who's That Man with Mr. Lincoln, Mommy?

Who's That Man with Mr. Lincoln, Mommy?
Copyright © 2018 John Darrin
Cover Art: Jeff Danziger
Cover Design: Jane Perini, Thunder Mountain Design
Book Design: Jane Perini, Thunder Mountain Design

ISBN 978-1-7327426-0-4

DEDICATION
Claire Waggoner for the inspiration to write again and
supporting me when I became the deadline monster.

Nele Berner for the absurd idea to write a children's book.
Bet this is not what she expected.

Josh & Christina for their expert advice and constant support.

ACKNOWLEDGEMENTS
All the contributing editorial cartoonists for their creativity, patience, and dedication.
Jane Perini for cover and book design under severe deadline pressure.

Who's **That Man** with Mr. Lincoln, Mommy?

~~PARENT'S~~ A Child's Guide to the Trump Presidency

LINCOLN MEMORIAL

TRUMP MEMORIAL HOTEL & CASINO

A PARODY BY JOHN DARRIN

ILLUSTRATED BY 24 AWARD-WINNING EDITORIAL CARTOONISTS

CONTENTS

Thank you for your interest in *Who's That Man with Mr. Lincoln, Mommy?* Without the creative contributions of 24 award-winning cartoonists, this book would be a rant, not a work of art. As it is, I have never worked so intensely on a book before, and a lot of that was due to trying to wrangle 24 award-winning cartoonists.

The courage and tenacity of these gifted artists, agreeing to lend their brilliance and incisiveness to the cause of truth has been both rewarding and motivating. The project began as my own need to respond to, to push back against, the daily degradation and division this administration has perpetrated on America, and I hope with their help, we have done something worthwhile.

The book's structure and content were built around the notion that nothing communicates as quickly nor as persuasively as an image that compels, that defines a message in one drawing—often with no need for words. With the decline of print journalism, the editorial cartoon has declined, and that is a pity. So I hope that you will pass this book along, in fact or in conversation, and echo my respect and admiration for these fine cartoonists and the important work they do.

Enjoy the book, and take both heart and motivation from its messages. And the most important one—you can't take a day off from democracy.

Nick Anderson

"An editorial cartoonist, fundamentally, should be anti-establishment."

At Ohio State University Anderson was the editorial cartoonist for the school's newspaper, winning the Charles M. Schulz Award. After an internship at *The Louisville Courier-Journal* he spent 15 years there before joining the *Houston Chronicle*. He is syndicated by the Washington Post Writer's Group. Anderson pioneered a unique method of coloring his cartoons, creating digital paintings of subtle textures and striking images. He won the Pulitzer Prize, the Sigma Delta Chi award, two Fischetti Awards, and the Berryman Award. In his spare time, Anderson enjoys mountain biking, cycling, lacrosse and kayaking.

Our story begins with a family on a vacation in Washington. The parents, Trump supporters both, are taking the kids for a walk around The Mall and environs, showing them American history.

And all the while trying to make the absurd and deceitful activities of the Trump Administration sound good and right, with the guileless innocence and instinctive perception of children deflating the hypocrisy of the message.

BILLY: Who's that man with Mr. Lincoln, Mommy?

MOTHER: That's President Trump, Billy. He's our second greatest President. Although many people say he is the greatest. I don't know. It could be true. I think so.

SUZIE: Why is he so great?

MOTHER: Well, Suzie, there are so many reasons. Why don't we play a game and see if we can figure it out?

FATHER: How about the alphabet game? We'll find a reason for every letter while we walk around The Mall and see all the interesting monuments.

MOTHER: Good idea, Sean. Why don't you start?

FATHER: An "A" word to start. I know! **Alternative Facts.** A fact is something that is true. Facts are the basis of all of our knowledge. For example, "It's raining" is a fact if there are clouds in the sky and drops of water falling. But there are times when the facts don't mean what you need them to mean.

SUZIE: I like to play in the rain.

FATHER: OK. Let's say you want to go out and play but Mommy says no because it's raining. You say, "No, it isn't, Mommy. God made the sun shine on me so I can play." That is called an alternative fact, and President Trump invented those. They are a very valuable tool if Mommy is too lazy to look out the window.

BILLY: I can tell Gramma that I got straight A's on my report card and that I am the smartest kid in my class. She will think that I have the best brain! Cool.

FATHER: But, Billy, the fact is you had mostly B's, and even that C.

BILLY: I don't care! I'm telling Gramma they were A's! She's old and forgets things. She'll believe me.

Nick Anderson

"**An editorial cartoonist, fundamentally, should be anti-establishment.**"

At Ohio State University Anderson was the editorial cartoonist for the school's newspaper, winning the Charles M. Schulz Award. After an internship at *The Louisville Courier-Journal* he spent 15 years there before joining the *Houston Chronicle*. He is syndicated by the Washington Post Writer's Group. Anderson pioneered a unique method of coloring his cartoons, creating digital paintings of subtle textures and striking images. He won the Pulitzer Prize, the Sigma Delta Chi award, two Fischetti Awards, and the Berryman Award. In his spare time, Anderson enjoys mountain biking, cycling, lacrosse and kayaking.

FATHER: Your turn, Sarah. Gimme a B!

MOTHER: This one is easy. B is for **Bigly.** That's one of President Trump's best words. And he has all the best words. Like covfefe. Bigly is when something is bigger and better than anything else like it.

BILLY: Like the snow fort we built last winter? We crushed everyone.

MOTHER: Even better than that, Billy. Bigly is when your snow fort is bigger and better than every other one that has ever been built by anybody in the whole, wide world.

BILLY: But it was bigger and better.

MOTHER: Than the other kid's, yes. Let me show you an example. See the Washington Monument over there? That was built for our first President, George Washington, and it's the biggest monument. When they build a monument to President Trump, it will be bigly and tower over everything else here.

SUZIE: What's a cofifi?

MOTHER: Good question. Suzie. The fake news said President Trump made a stupid mistake, but he said only some special people know the meaning. It's a secret.

Monte Wolverton

"At its heart, the function of an editorial cartoonist is mockery. Politicians and celebrities ascend to near divinity. We tear them back down to reality—maybe lower."

In addition to two decades of editorial cartooning, Monte Wolverton has authored several novels, been active in magazine publishing, and worked in advertising and graphic design. His cartoons are currently available in hundreds of publications through Caglecartoons. For some of us, he will be remembered for his many contributions to MAD magazine. He is son of legendary illustrator Basil Wolverton.

FATHER: For C, I think **Collusion** is a good word. You see, kids, when several people get together and cooperate to achieve an important goal, like, say to win an election, that's called collusion.

BILLY: Does President Trump collusion?

FATHER: No, Billy, there was no collusion. That would be wrong because collusion means they were secretly trying to do something that is against the law, and President Trump wouldn't break the law. He doesn't have to. He's the President and he can ignore the law.

BILLY: I'm going to collusion with my friends to make recess twice as long.

MOTHER: But, Billy, your teacher won't let you.

BILLY: Then what good is collusion?

MOTHER: Well, Billy, collusion only works if you have a really good plan and very powerful friends to help you. And you have to keep it a secret so people won't know what you're doing and will think everything is alright.

BILLY: When I'm President I'm going to ignore every law I don't like!"

Steve Artley

"An effective editorial cartoon can be funny, but if it doesn't deliver a message with bite, efficacy is diminished."

Steve Artley's award-winning cartoons have appeared in *USA Today*, *Newsweek*, the *Washington Post*, and *The New York Times*, and in Best of anthologies from *TIME Magazine*, and the *Washington Post*. He is active in the business, serving on the Board of the Association of American Editorial Cartoonists, and is a member of the National Cartoonists Society and the National Press Club. Artley lives in Alexandria, VA and works out of his studio in Old Town.

MOTHER: My D word is **Deficit.** A deficit is when you don't have enough of something. Like if you don't have enough money to buy a new car so you have to borrow money. You have to pay it back and if you can't you have to borrow some more, and your deficit gets bigger.

SUZIE: Do we have enough money, Mommy?

FATHER: Yes, Suzie. We have plenty of money. Daddy earns enough money to pay for all our stuff.

SUZIE: What happens if you lose your job like Linda's daddy?

BILLY: They come and take your house and kick you out.

SUZIE: Will President Trump lose America and get us kicked out, Daddy?

FATHER: No, of course not. President Trump knows more about borrowing money than anyone. He can just declare bankruptcy and all the money he owes disappears. Lots of people lose their money, but President Trump wins.

SUZIE: Will America declare krupsie?

FATHER: No, honey. America can always borrow more money from places like China. America will never run out of money. Really.

Ed Hall

"The sting of a political cartoon is never lost upon those who know what they've done."

Ed Hall holds a Masters of Fine Art from the University of Florida which he chose to apply to skewering those needing it through editorial cartoons. He has worked in the Jacksonville, FL area during the last two decades and won numerous awards and competitions during that time, the Green Eyeshade and Florida Press Club among them. He is syndicated to newspapers and other venues across N. America by Artizans, and his work has appeared in papers and galleries worldwide, including *Le Monde, Le Temps,* and *Eulenspiegel.*

FATHER: I'll give you a hard word that starts with E. **Emoluments.** It's a big word for getting paid for doing something for someone, like when you mow lawns, Billy. President Trump is a very rich man because he has hotels that rich men from all over the world pay a lot to use.

MOTHER: And rich women, too, Sean.

FATHER: Yes, dear. The rich men often bring their wives with them.

BILLY: So it's like all of his big-deal friends are giving him money. That's cool.

FATHER: Not exactly, Billy. The President is not allowed to take emoluments. People might try to use gifts and money to get him to do what they want, not what's best for America. So he gave his businesses to his two sons to run. They can't do favors because they're not the President.

BILLY: If I was rich, I'd share all my money with you and Mommy.

MOTHER: That's so sweet, Billy. I'm sure President Trump's children feel the same way about him.

SUZIE: I want to be a rich woman when I grow up.

MOTHER: Yes, dear, and you can be. Take care of yourself and keep yourself beautiful and you will meet the right man and you can be rich, too. That's how our First Lady did it.

"I believe a political cartoonist should 'comfort the afflicted and afflict the comfortable.'
I try to do it with humor, and I'm never more serious than when I'm joking."

Stuart Carlson is an award-winning cartoonist who, as a toddler, began his career by drawing in lipstick on the walls of his home. His art has improved since then and appeared in the *Milwaukee Journal Sentinel* for 25 years, garnering local and national awards, including the best editorial cartoonist in the US by the National Press Foundation. Carlson's work is syndicated to about 35 newspapers nationally, and has appeared in *Time*, *Newsweek*, the *New York Times* and the *Washington Post*.

Stuart Carlson

MOTHER: For the F word, I pick **Fake News**.

BILLY: You said the F word.

MOTHER: Stop being silly or we won't play anymore. Remember when you fibbed to everyone about how many friends came to your birthday party? You were grounded for a whole week. The news is very important so we know what's happening in our world. Fake news is when the media doesn't pay enough attention to alternative facts and just talks about regular facts. Pretty soon, people are reading and thinking things that you don't want them to."

BILLY: See. I didn't fib. I just told you fake news.

MOTHER: That wasn't fake news, Billy. That was a fib.

BILLY: How do you know what is fake news?

MOTHER: Well first, it has to be about President Trump. I think all the rest of the news is fine. Second, it has to disagree with him and his policies. Just watch Fox News and you'll know it's real.

A MONUMENT TO THE PRESIDENT WHO COULD NOT TELL A LIE

A MONUMENT TO THE PRESIDENT WHO COULD NOT TELL THE TRUTH

FAKE NEWS

Joe Heller

"Opinion, humor and illustration, distilled down to make a point a reader can comprehend in seconds. Editorial cartooning is mightier than the pen or the sword."

Joe Heller was the editorial cartoonist for the *Green Bay Press-Gazette* for 3 decades and currently syndicates his work to over 400 newspapers throughout the U.S. His award-winning cartoons have been published in the *Washington Post, USA Today, The Denver Post, Los Angeles Times, Newsweek, Time* and *The Christian Science Monitor.* Joe was born and raised in Wisconsin and is a graduate of the University of Wisconsin-Milwaukee. His home is in Green Bay. And yes, he owns a cheesehead hat.

FATHER: G is for **Golf.** President Trump is a great golfer and plays more golf than any other President. He is so good that he can play two games every week and still have time to run the country.

SUZIE: Daddy, when you play golf you're gone for the whole day.

MOTHER: Not to mention how much it costs.

FATHER: Each game takes a lot of time, Suzie. And yes, golf is expensive. But you know I need to unwind after a hard week. It costs me a lot less than President Trump. He spends over $5 million for each round.

BILLY: Wow! He must be very rich.

FATHER: Yes, he is, Billy. But he doesn't have to pay for it. We pay for it because we know he needs his relaxation so he can make our country great. And he meets with very important people while playing and they help make America great again, too.

BILLY: For that much money he ought to make America great forever.

"While I set out to be a political cartoonist, sadly I increasingly feel like an elegist for my country."

Jen Sorensen is the first woman to win the Herblock Prize, and was a 2017 Pulitzer Prize Finalist. She also received the Robert F. Kennedy Journalism Award, National Cartoonists Society Award, and the Inkpot Award from San Diego Comic-Con for career achievement in comic arts. Her cartoons appear in twenty-five alternative newspapers around the USA and have been published in *The Nation, The Progressive, Politico,* and digital outlets including Daily Kos, Truthout, and The Nib. Jen attended the University of Virginia where she studied cultural anthropology.

Jen Sorensen

MOTHER: And he is not just a great President. He is a great man, too. So my H word is **Heart**, because President Trump has the biggest heart of anyone. He runs a foundation that raises millions of dollars to help charities all across the country. They give away almost a million dollars every year. And some of that is President Trump's personal money.

BILLY: Who else's money does he give away?

MOTHER: He gets his other rich friends and people who like him to contribute.

BILLY: Who does he give the money to?

MOTHER: To lots of needy people. He buys great art like his portrait and he helps elect people he likes. His favorite charity is the Police Athletic League, They help needy kids stay out of trouble.

SUZIE: He must love kids.

MOTHER: Yes he does. He made sure that his police protected kids coming alone to America by putting them in kids-only camps. Imagine how much fun that must be. They say it was one of the greatest acts of charity and generosity in the world.

SUZIE: How did they lose their parents?

MOTHER: They didn't exactly lose them. They were trying to sneak into America and got arrested because they broke the law.

HEARTLESS

Barbara Dale

"Editorial cartoonists are on the Front Line of defending the First Amendment. They're the bravest people I know."

In addition to her work in editorial cartooning, Barbara is one of the pioneers of alternative greeting cards. The *Washington Post* described her and her generation of card designers as having, "changed the face of the nearly 7 billion cards Americans sent to each other last year." In the book, *A Gallery of Rogues: Cartoonists' Self-Caricatures* she's described as, "Specializing in off-the-wall humor of the taste-expanding variety." She's the co-author and illustrator of two humor books, *The Working Woman Book* and *The Joys of Motherhood.*

FATHER: So let's do an I word. What do you think, Sarah? Immigration? Investigation?

MOTHER: How about **Impeachment**, Sean?

FATHER: Good one! Impeachment is what politicians do at the end of a rigged witch hunt to get rid of someone who is bothering them. So they get together with their friends and use fake news to accuse someone of crimes. Then they vote to make him go or let him stay.

SUZIE: Can I impeachment Melissa? She's always picking on me.

MOTHER: I wish! Her mother is a *real* witch.

SUZIE: Let's go hunt her!

FATHER: Not that kind of a hunt. A witch hunt is when people chase after something that isn't really there.

BILLY: Like a ghost.

FATHER: No, it's like when you need someone to blame for things you don't like. President Trump's enemies don't want him to make America great so they are trying to blame him for made-up things. Like cheating to get elected by having the Russians hack into our computers to change the results. They say that so they can impeach him and throw him out. Even the FBI is trying. But President Trump knows better. He found some very fat man in New Jersey who did it, but no one believes him.

IMPEACHMENT IS A POLITICAL PROCESS—

IS IT AN IMPEACHABLE OFFENSE?

IT DEPENDS.

NOT A LEGAL ONE.

IT HAS THE TRAPPINGS OF A LEGAL PROCEDING:

COUNTS

"CHARGES"

"HIGH CRIMES AND MISDEMEANORS"

"TRIAL" (IN THE HOUSE)

AYES HAVE IT

"CONVICTION" (IN THE SENATE)

IN "THE FEDERALIST PAPERS," ALEXANDER HAMILTON EXPLAINED THAT THE PURPOSE OF IMPEACHMENT IS TO ADDRESS

"INJURIES DONE IMMEDIATELY TO... SOCIETY."

It's about conduct... demeanor... comportment.

RICHARD NIXON AND BILL CLINTON WERE HEAVY LIFTS. SOMEONE LIKE TRUMP IS **EXACTLY** WHAT THE FOUNDERS HAD IN MIND.

@ ★ # !
■ ▲ ◉ ∅
🌲 ⚡ @ !!!

Ted Rall

"Just when America needs political cartooning more than ever, there are fewer political cartoonists than ever. It almost feels like a conspiracy."

Ted Rall is one of the most widely syndicated editorial cartoonists in America. His cartoons have appeared in hundreds of publications around the world, including *Rolling Stone, Time, Newsweek, Esquire*, the *Washington Post, San Francisco Chronicle, Los Angeles Times* and many others. Rall is also a graphic novelist, having won prizes for his works To Afghanistan and Back, Snowden and Bernie. He is a graduate of Columbia University and editor of the three-volume cartoon anthology Attitudes.

MOTHER: I have a J word. **Jared**. He's married to the President's beautiful daughter, Ivanka. He is also a very successful businessman and helps President Trump run the country.

SUZIE: President Trump needs help?

MOTHER: Yes, of course he does, honey. Running the country is a very big job, and Jared really helps. He can do things in secret with the Russians that President Trump can't because people are always watching him and lying about what he is doing.

BILLY: I thought the Russians were bad.

MOTHER: Well, they used to be, but President Trump is trying to make them our friend. They have lots of money that can help President Trump do more good. And right now, Jared is solving all the problems with the Jews and Arabs, and he's organizing our whole government to do their work better. He even has time to fix our criminal justice system so people like his father will be more comfortable in prison.

BILLY: His Dad's in prison?

MOTHER: Yes, he is. He was a New York City real estate developer like President Trump and he did bad things that took other people's money. That business is very shady and it's a good thing President Trump is so open and honest.

"I believe a political cartoonist should 'comfort the afflicted and afflict the comfortable.'
I try to do it with humor, and I'm never more serious than when I'm joking."

Stuart Carlson is an award-winning cartoonist who, as a toddler, began his career by drawing in lipstick on the walls of his home. His art has improved since then and appeared in the *Milwaukee Journal Sentinel* for 25 years, garnering local and national awards, including the best editorial cartoonist in the US by the National Press Foundation. Carlson's work is syndicated to about 35 newspapers nationally, and has appeared in *Time, Newsweek,* the *New York Times* and the *Washington Post.*

Stuart Carlson

FATHER: Alright, a K word. I've got one that even you won't know, Sarah. **Kakistocracy**. That is a government that uses only people the leader can trust to run the country. That is much more important than using experienced government workers or qualified experts, or even honest citizens.

BILLY: That must be why my teacher got her job. She's stupid but she's always sucking up to the Principal.

MOTHER: I don't think so, Billy. Teachers have to go to college for a lot of years and learn things and get trained.

BILLY: But Dad just said loyalty is more important.

FATHER: Well, Billy, there are many loyal people who can do the jobs President Trump needs done and they don't have to be experts. For example, you don't need to be a scientist or engineer to run the EPA. There are plenty of those already working there. President Trump needs someone in charge who will make sure everyone does things the way he wants them done and not be brainwashed by fake science like climate change.

SUZIE: But I heard you tell Mommy that your boss is an idiot. Are you loyal to him?

FATHER: Well, yes. I have to be or I would lose my job.

BILLY: Ha ha. You work in a cactuscrazy.

Clay Jones

"My job is not to anger readers. It's my job to make readers think. If they get angry along the way, that's just an added bonus."

Spanning the globe, Clay Jones has worked for newspapers from Virginia to Cost Rica to Hawaii, getting awards all along the way. He left Creators Syndicate to create Claytoonz.com, and he's currently syndicating to over 50 newspapers nationally and internationally. He's been featured in *The New York Times*, the *Washington Post*, the *Los Angeles Times*, *Newsweek*, *Politico*, and shown on CNN and MSNBC. Clay lives in Fredericksburg, VA, plays sloppy guitar, drinks too much coffee, and remains goofy and annoying.

MOTHER: So you see, a kakistocracy needs **Loyalty**, so that is my L word. Loyalty means you help and protect someone no matter what, whether they are right or wrong. If all the other kids in Suzie's class started picking on her, you would protect her and stand up to them, right Billy? That's loyalty to your sister."

SUZIE: Why would they pick on me? I didn't do anything.

MOTHER: No, honey. Of course you didn't. I was just making up an example. President Trump didn't do anything wrong, either, but people pick on him anyway. Like when all those horrid women made up nasty stories about him. His family and friends stood up for him and called them liars.

SUZIE: Why do they lie about him?

MOTHER: I don't know. Sometimes people are just not nice. Like that lying FBI man who said bad things about President Trump. Even if President Trump did ask him for loyalty, what's wrong with that? You should be willing to swear loyalty to the President. Especially President Trump.

BILLY: Don't worry, Mom. I'd take good care of Suzie. If they ever pick on her, I'll beat them up.

FATHER: Good for you, Billy. It's very important to never let anyone think you are weak.

Phil Hands

"When I was a kid, I decided to become a cartoonist because I thought it would be an easy way to make a lot of money. I was wrong."

Phil Hands is the editorial cartoonist for the *Wisconsin State Journal*. His cartoons have appeared in *USA Today, Newsweek, Time* and the *Washington Post* and are syndicated nationally by Tribune Content Agency. Phil has won a number of state and national awards and was the 2012 recipient of the Sigma Delta Chi award for editorial cartooning. In his spare time he enjoys drinking coffee, eating cheese and being cold.

FATHER: I've got a great M word. In fact, it's the best M word. President Trump says he has the best words, and it's true. And when there is no best word, he invents one. So the M word in **MAGA**. It stands for Make America Great Again, which is just what President Trump is doing.

SUZIE: Does that mean America isn't great right now?

FATHER: No, sweetie. Of course America is great. It's just that, well, our last President did some silly stuff and let some wrong things happen and President Trump has to fix them. Like, he let all of these foreigners stay in the country when they didn't belong here. They're taking jobs from us and getting free money and doctors to take care of them and everything. So, President Trump is making them go away.

BILLY: But Aunt Elaine says her family brought her here from China because America is great. Does she have to go away?"

FATHER: No, son. She's not really your aunt and she's an American citizen just like us. She was eight, just about your age, when she came here. She didn't speak any English but that didn't stop her from going to the best schools and getting good jobs and helping make America great.

BILLY: So she is a good foreigner. Cool.

Pat Bagley

"I believe in the Platonic Ideal of a cartoon. Somewhere out there is a perfect cartoon which will destroy Trump. I work each day with the goal of finding it."

In the dubious but remarkable records category, Pat Bagley is the longest-lived, continuously-employed, full-time political cartoonist in America. During a finance class at BYU, Bagley doodled a political cartoon which was reprinted in *Time Magazine*. His first published cartoon. In his four decades drawing, Bagley has created more than 10,000 cartoons and has won many prestigious awards and was a finalist for the Pulitzer. His work goes out to 800 publications worldwide through syndication by politicalcartoons. com.

MOTHER: I'm going to pick **NAFTA** as the N word. That's the name of a trade agreement America has with Mexico and Canada to buy and sell stuff. But the Mexicans and Canadians used the deal to cheat America out of tons of money. President Trump put a stop to that.

BILLY: I must have had a trade agreement with the other guys. We traded baseball cards. When Jason tried to cheat, I punched him. Why don't we just punch Canada and Mexico?

MOTHER: That's sort of what President Trump is doing. It's called a trade war. We charge them money to bring stuff into America, and then they charge us money to send stuff into Canada. And because America is big and powerful, he says trade wars are easy to win.

BILLY: If I try to make Jason give me more for my cards, he just gets cards from the other guys. I think I should just punch him and take the cards I want. Punching Jason is easy. He's a pussy.

MOTHER: Billy! Do not use that word unless you're talking about a cat. That's not nice. And you are not to punch Jason.

BILLY: Then how I can win? This doesn't sound so easy.

Ingrid Rice

"The news media is not the enemy of the people. The news media is the enemy of those who have something to hide from the people."

Canadian cartoonist Ingrid Rice's lifelong contempt for authority figures led her into the murky netherworld of political cartooning. A never-ending stream of subject matter has kept her there. She began her career freelancing to the *Vancouver Sun* where her cartoons enraged xenophobes, feminists, assisted suicide opponents, and during which time she appeared before the British Columbia Press Council and was found to be "reprehensible," a source of immense pride.

FATHER: O is for **Obama**.

SUZIE: What's wrong, Daddy?

FATHER: Nothing, sweetie. I just have a bad taste in my mouth. Obama was President before President Trump. He was a bad President and that's why President Trump has to Make America Great Again. He did things like let lots of foreign kids stay here when they didn't belong. And he wanted to get rid of all our guns so criminals could hurt us. And worst of all, he created a socialist system to give health care to everyone.

SUZIE: One of the boys in my class said he just went to the doctor for the first time ever. I didn't believe him. But he said his parents couldn't pay for one so he never went.

FATHER: Well, that's just silly. His parents should know better. They can always use the emergency room at the hospital. But you know what was worse? He cheated to get elected! He wasn't even born in America, and he was a secret Muslim who hated God.

MOTHER: And his wife! She believed those women who tried to hurt President Trump, and she didn't like him having a fun talk with his friends on a bus. We are very happy to be rid of both of them.

"It is easy to mock authority, and humor can entertain with little relevance. The truly successful political cartoonist informs, motivates, and inspires the reader."

Joe Sutliff has been cartooning since 1968 and his work has appeared in books, magazines, the Internet, the World Wide Web, the Dark Web, public bathrooms, and anywhere else he could scribble. He has received a number of awards, proving any judge can be bought, and he continues to search for new and innovative ways to convince people that he is no danger to society. He self-syndicates until his pen gives out or bourbon becomes free.

Joe Sutliff

MOTHER: But let's talk about a P word. Putin? Pussy? No, everyone already talks about those words. I want to talk about **Puerto Rico**. Nobody remembers them anymore. Puerto Rico is a little island somewhere that got destroyed by a big hurricane, and now they want Americans to pay to fix it back up. President Trump has been very courageous and caring about them, although I'm not sure why, sending them all kinds of help and lots of our tax money.

BILLY: Did they fix it?

MOTHER: No! Of course not. They always want more and more. It's not like Texas or Florida where American homes and businesses were destroyed. Where were the Puerto Ricans when those states got hit by big hurricanes? They didn't lift a finger to help us. They should look to their own country and government for help, not America.

SUZIE: But Mommy, in school the teacher told us about the hurricane there and he said Puerto Rico belongs to America.

FATHER: That's nonsense, Suzie. Your teacher was mistaken. They are not part of America. America has fifty states, and I guarantee Puerto Rico isn't one of them. You tell your teacher that. But you do it respectfully.

Keith Knight

"Wait a second, you get paid for doing this?"
- Jasper Knight Age 9

Keith Knight, winner of the Glyph, Harvey, and Inkpot Awards, is a spectacular cartoonist whose *Knight Life* comic strip is read nationwide in such newspapers as the *Washington Post, San Francisco Chronicle*, and the *San Diego Union Tribune*. Keef's funny yet hard-hitting cartoons in his webcomic series, (T)hink and The K Chronicles, led him to be named one of the 2015 NAACP History Makers. Knight is the illustrator of the critically acclaimed tween book, *Jake the Fake Keeps It Real*. His new collection of Knight Life strips is called *Do The Knight Thing*.

FATHER: A Q word. That's a very hard one. The only thing I can think of is, well, adult. What do you think, Sarah?

MOTHER: You mean **Queer**, don't you? Well, I'm sure they hear worse than that in school and we should make sure they know the truth. Just be, I don't know, clean.

FATHER: OK. Well, kids, you know that a marriage is between a man and a woman, right? That's God's law. But sometimes people get all mixed up and think that it's OK for two men or two women to get married. It isn't, and we call those people queer.

SUZIE: But there is a girl in my class who says she has two Mommy's. Are they queer?

BILLY: And my teacher has a man friend who sometimes picks him up after school. Is he queer, too?

FATHER: Well, yes, they probably are. I didn't know about your teacher. Did you, Sarah?

MOTHER: No, of course not. We need to bring this to the attention of the PTA!

MAGA
MISTREATING ALL GAY AMERICANS

Randy Bish

"Proud to have been slinging ink for over 30 years and saddened to see what has happened to our government in that time."

Randy Bish drew cartoons for the *Pittsburgh Tribune-Review* for over 31 years. Today, his work is distributed via Pennsylvania NewsMedia and Cagle Cartoons. Randy's cartoons have appeared in *USA Today*, on Good Morning America, Fox News, C-Span, CNN, and the refrigerator doors of his many fans. He has won the Clarion Award and several Golden Quill Awards. His cartoons may be found in the Charles Schulz and Jimmy Stewart Museums, the Ford Presidential Library, Newseum, and the Heinz History Center.

MOTHER: My R word is **Russia**. Russia is a far-off land that has always been ruled by very bad men. They are our enemy and have tried to hurt America many times. They have nuclear weapons and missiles that could destroy the world, and only America can stop them. President Trump is secretly trying to be friends with the Russians to make the world a better place for him and his friends and all Americans. The Russians even helped President Trump with our elections! Still, there are some people who don't want peace because they don't want President Trump to get any credit for it and helping the world.

BILLY: If it's far away, how did they help President Trump?

MOTHER: They used the Internet! That was very smart. They found lots of emails that President Trump's enemies tried to hide and they showed them to everyone. Then they got on Facebook just like you and your friends and told all the Americans about how bad President Trump's enemies are, and how good he is.

BILLY: If Russia has always been our enemy, why did they help President Trump?

MOTHER: Because President Trump is such good friends with their President, Mr. Putin.

SUZIE: I like Russians, too. I like their dressing on my lettuce.

Robert Matson

"The only thing necessary for the triumph of evil is that good cartoonists draw nothing."

R.J. Matson is the editorial cartoonist at Roll Call and previously worked at the *St. Louis Post-Dispatch*, *The New York Observer*, *States News Service*, and *The Washington Monthly*. His cartoons and illustrations have appeared in *The New Yorker*, *The Nation*, *MAD Magazine*, *The Daily News*, *The Washington Post*, and many other publications. Along the way he won numerous regional awards and in 2007, he drew Time's *Best Cartoon of the Year*. He received a B.A. from Columbia University and was a visiting student at Pembroke College, Oxford University.

FATHER: My S word is another acronym – **SCOTUS**. That stands for the Supreme Court of the United States. You guys know what a court is. You've seen it on Judge Judy. The Supreme Court is like the most powerful court. They make the final decisions if people won't accept what Judge Judy and other courts decide.

SUZIE: She's mean. Always telling people to shut up.

FATHER: Well, the Supreme Court isn't. They are our nine best judges and they are judges for their whole life, so it's even more important that they are the best and that they act according to our Constitution and not their own political views. That's called partisanship and they don't do that.

BILLY: Who decides they are the best?

FATHER: The President. And then Congress has to approve them.

BILLY: What if they don't? Approve.

FATHER: That happened when our last President was a Democrat and tried to appoint a bad judge. Fortunately the Republicans had enough votes to block him.

BILLY: Isn't that partisanship?

FATHER: Your turn, Sarah. What's your T word?

Jeff Danziger

"An effective political cartoon should form an image in the reader's mind that explains, provokes, convinces, cajoles, or simply entertains. I've been doing this for 35 years, and I have no idea what I will do when I grow up."

Jeff began drawing and writing for the *Rutland Herald* in 1975 and then became a cartoonist for the *New York Daily News*. He has worked at *Christian Science Monitor* in Boston and is now syndicated by the *New York Times*. He has twice been a Pulitzer Finalist and has been awarded an Overseas Press Club Prize, the Herblock Prize, and the Thomas Nast Award.

MOTHER: You will know all about my T word. **Tweet**. Long ago, whenever the President wanted to tell everyone his important thoughts, he would make a long, boring speech or send a letter called a Press Release. But Twitter changed all of that. Now the President can tell everyone how to think in just 280 letters from his phone anytime he wants. Even at 3 o'clock in the morning when everyone you know is sound asleep in their beds.

SUZIE: We tweeted in school, Mommy.

BILLY: Yeah. They set up some cell phones in the auditorium and everybody got a chance to send a tweet about something important.

FATHER: That's great kids but let your Mother finish telling you about some of President Trump's amazing tweets. Like when he told about fake news and the Russia witch hunt and the corrupt Democrats. Go ahead, Sarah.

MOTHER: No, that's OK, Sean. You kids tell us what you tweeted.

SUZIE: I tweeted to the kids who got shot at that school. I told them I was very sorry, and I hoped they were alright.

BILLY: Mine was for homeless people. I told them about the new shelter they built in our town.

MOTHER: That was very sweet. Both of you. I'm sure President Trump has sent tweets just like that.

Robert Matson

"The only thing necessary for the triumph of evil is that good cartoonists draw nothing."

R.J. Matson is the editorial cartoonist at Roll Call and previously worked at the *St. Louis Post-Dispatch, The New York Observer, States News Service,* and *The Washington Monthly.* His cartoons and illustrations have appeared in *The New Yorker, The Nation, MAD Magazine, The Daily News, The Washington Post,* and many other publications. Along the way he won numerous regional awards and in 2007, he drew Time's *Best Cartoon of the Year.* He received a B.A. from Columbia University and was a visiting student at Pembroke College, Oxford University.

FATHER: OK, my turn. Did you know that by just adding "un" in front of a word, you can make it mean the exact opposite? If we put "un" in front of "fit" we get **Unfit**, and that's my U word. A President must be fit to be our leader. He must be able to take care of our country and to make life safe and free for all Americans. He must be smart and understand world problems.

SUZIE: Did he have to take a test?

FATHER: No test. President Trump is a very stable genius. He knows the military better than the generals. He respects women more than anybody. He understands our economy better than those financial geniuses.

SUZIE: How do we know if he didn't take a test? I have to take tests.

FATHER: Because nobody in history has been more fit to be President. Not even President Lincoln.

BILLY: But President Lincoln freed the slaves and won the Civil War.

FATHER: Well, Billy, we don't have slaves any more. And when some black people and white people were fighting President Trump told everyone that there were good people on both sides and they should stop fighting.

BILLY: What happens if you put "un" in front of "President"?

Rick McKee

"I'm fortunate somebody pays me to do what I love. Hopefully, I'll never have to go get a real job."

From doodling pictures of his high school principal to skewering the President in the newspapers of America, Rick McKee has been cartooning in one form or another all of his life. Working at *The Augusta Chronicle* and syndicated to more than 850 other papers, McKee is one of the most reprinted cartoonists in America. McKee won first place in the Ranan Lurie/U.N. cartoon competition and is the U.S. Ambassador for United Sketches, an international organization to support freedom of expression and cartoonists in exile.

MOTHER: I'm going to pick **Vote** as our V word. In America every real citizen gets to vote to elect our leaders. And when we voted last time, we elected President Trump by an overwhelming number of votes.

BILLY: But my teacher said he lost by three million votes. How did he get to be President if he lost?

MOTHER: Well, Billy, that's not true. He didn't lose. First of all, those votes were illegal. President Trump's enemies were able sneak people in to vote because we have been weak about enforcing our laws. The President is going to investigate this and I'm sure we'll hear very soon about how to solve the problem of all these illegal voters ruining our democracy.

BILLY: Did they subtract all of those votes so President Trump could win?

MOTHER: No. That would be impossible with millions of votes. But we have a special system called the Electoral College where special people from every state choose the President. And President Trump won there by a huge number.

SUZIE: Can I be one of those special people when I grow up?

MOTHER: Of course you can, honey. You just need to have powerful friends. Or you can give them a lot of money.

Rob Tornoe

"The great Pat Oliphant is quoted as saying he sees himself as an artist who happens to do cartoons. I see myself as a political pundit who happens to doodle."

Rob Tornoe is a cartoonist and writer based in Delaware where he currently works for the Philadelphia Inquirer covering the media and drawing sports cartoons. His work has appeared in numerous publications, including *The New York Times*, the *Washington Post* and *USA Today*. Tornoe has won several awards for his editorial cartooning, including "Best Cartoon" by the NJ Society of Professional Journalists. In 2008, his cartoon criticizing the Iraq War was featured on the floor of the House of Representatives. In addition to cartooning, Tornoe writes for Editor & Publisher about the media and the business of syndication.

FATHER: Do you see that black wall, right over there? That is a memorial to our soldiers who fought in the Viet Nam war to stop Communism. And we did. President Trump wants to build a wall, too, so my W word is **Wall**.

BILLY: Did President Trump fight the Communists? I bet he would have beaten them all by himself.

FATHER: No, Billy. He couldn't. President Trump has an injury to his feet called bone spurs. He stayed home and built his business with his Italian and Russian friends in New York. But he is going to build a big, beautiful wall to keep the bad people from Mexico out. And you know what? It won't cost America anything! He is going to make Mexico pay for it.

BILLY: How can he do that, Daddy?

FATHER: Well, America is a big, important country and Mexico is a poor country run by bad men who work for the drug dealers. They have to do what President Trump says or he will punish them.

BILLY: At school, I have to do what Vincent says or he will beat me up. Will President Trump beat Mexico up?

FATHER: Yes, Billy, I think he'll try.

Joel Pett

"Stare at blank paper. Think, doodle, try things. When you're finished, maybe you've created something memorable or interesting....if not, there's plenty more blank paper."

Four-time Pulitzer finalist and one-time winner, Joel Pett's sharp-edged political cartoons have appeared in publications worldwide, including the *Washington Post, New York Times, Los Angeles Times, Times of London,* and *USA Today.* Pett also received the Robert F. Kennedy Journalism Award and five Global Media Awards as well as an Emmy for television commentary. A sometime stand-up comic, Pett has shared his simple and provocative humor at dozens of venues, including the Newseum, Indiana University, Ohio State University, Brandeis University and more.

MOTHER: There is a good reason for the wall besides the drugs and crime and illegal votes, kids. President Trump has the best qualities and one of the most important is my X word – **Xenophobia**. That is when you love your own people above all others, and President Trump loves us more than the Mexicans or Africans or Asians or Arabs.

SUZIE: But Mommy, we have some of those people in my class at school, and I like them. Elena is from Mexico and she's my friend.

MOTHER: I know, Suzie, but those are the good ones who want to be just like us. President Trump is finding all the others and sending them back to their own country. He has this really cool police called ICE. They go around and find all the bad Mexicans and Muslims and arrest them and send the away.

SUZIE: Why are they called ICE? Are they cold?

MOTHER: Not like cold "brrrrr." But cold like, "I don't care." That way they won't be sad when they send away families who might seem nice but are really trying to take our jobs.

BILLY: How can I get zenofob-ed? Are you born that way?

MOTHER: No, Billy. It's something your parents teach you, and we're doing that right now.

Darrin Bell

"**In 1791, a free black man, Benjamin Banneker, wrote to Thomas Jefferson that the nation was falling far short of the principles the founders professed. We've been writing that same letter ever since. In prose, poetry, song, film, and graffiti. And sometimes, in cartoons.**"

Darrin Bell has 24 years of editorial cartooning experience starting at the University of California, Berkeley, the *Los Angeles Times*, the *San Francisco Chronicle*, the *Oakland Tribune*, and other Bay Area News Group papers. He is an occasional contributor to *The New Yorker*. Bell creates the comic strips "Candorville" and "Rudy Park" for the Washington Post Writers Group, and has won the Berryman and Kennedy Awards

FATHER: It's my turn for the Y word. President Trump was a big TV star and he liked to say "you're fired" and kick people off his show when he didn't like them. So my Y word is **You're Fired**.

SUZIE: That's not nice. He should be nice to people.

FATHER: You can't always be nice, Suzie. People mess up or don't do what they're supposed to and you have to fire them.

SUZIE: Does President Trump still fire people because he doesn't like them?

FATHER: No, of course not. That's only on TV. He fires them because they aren't the best people for the job.

BILLY: You said before it's a cactuscrazy and he only hires people who are loyal to him, not because they're the best.

FATHER: I know it's confusing, but they're the best people for the job because they do what President Trump wants no matter what they think. President Trump gets to decide what is best and right. So you see, they are the best at obeying him.

SUZIE: Does your boss like you?

FATHER: I think so, but if I do my job well then there is no problem.

BILLY: I don't get it.

"Fortunately for my Physics career, science is more of an art than a science."

Al Goodwyn has a degree in Physics which came in handy for cartooning, publishing science-themed cartoons for technical publications for many years. His editorial cartooning began with the *Aiken Standard* newspaper and since then, his cartoons have appeared in the *Washington Examiner*, the *Washington Times*, *The Hill*, several local papers. He has illustrated several books (among them one of mine - JD) and provided cover illustrations for the *Washington Examiner*. Al has recently put away his science pen to focus on editorial cartoons that appear regularly in print.

Al Goodwyn

MOTHER: Wow. A Z word. Zealot, zeppelin, zero, zest, zigzag, zombie, zone, zoo, zucchini. I can't think of any Z word for President Trump.

FATHER: Zoom, zinc, zing, zip, zipper, zap. Wow, neither can I."

BILLY: I have a word! If President Trump can make up words whenever he wants, so can I.

MOTHER: OK, Billy. Go ahead.

BILLY: My Z word is **Zapoff**. It means I'm sick and tired of President Trump and I want to go have some fun.

"My first exposure to political satire was through music, so I wanted to be a folksinger. I realized that would be a difficult way to make a living, so I chose the second most impractical career — a cartoonist."

Jimmy Margulies is the Editorial Cartoonist for *amNEW YORK*. His cartoons have been published in *The New York Times, Washington Post, USA Today, Los Angeles Times, Time, Newsweek*, among others. And he has been featured on CNN, ABC Nightline, PBS and C-Span. His many awards include the Berryman, the National Headliner, the Fischetti, and four Clarions. He is proudly blacklisted by the NRA.

Jimmy Margulies

There are a lot of words we could have used, and we considered many.
Here they are, with the final selection left to the author and the cartoonist.

Alternative Facts	Fake News	Muslims	SCOTUS
Alt-right	Fox News	Mexicans	Shutdown
Authoritarian	Golf	Misogynist	Senate
Autocrat	Global warming	Morals/Morality	Syria
Arrogant	Heart (less)	Megalomaniac	Shithole
Anarchy	Hotel	Military	Sexual abuse
Bigly	Hillary	NAFTA	Tweet
Bankruptcy	Healthcare	Nepotism	Treason
Collusion	Impeachment	Narcissist	Tap (wire)
Covfefe	Immigration	Neo-Nazi	Tyranny
Corruption	Investigations	Nambia	Tantrums
Clinton	Instable/Instability	NRA	Terrorist
Cover-up	Incompetent	Obama	TPP
Complicit	Ignorant	Obstruction	Unfit
Chaos	Jared	Oligarchy	Unhinged
Conspiracy	Jobs	Puerto Rico	Unstable
Climate change	Kakistocracy	Putin	Unqualified
Deficit	Kim Jung Un	Pussy	Vote
Dotard	Kneel	Pardon	Venal
Drain the swamp	Kleptocracy	Queer	Vacation
Dreamers	Loyalty	Qualified	Wall
DACA	Lies/Liar	Qatar	Witch hunt
Emoluments	Leaks	Russia	Xenophobia
Electoral College	Loyalty	Racism	You're fired
Ego/Egocentric	Loser	Rapist	Yanukovych
Evil	MAGA	Refugees	Yuge
Erratic	Mar-A-Lago	Reckless	Zapoff

INDEX OF CARTOONISTS